I Believe...

POEMS OF FAITH FOR CHILDREN

Irma L. Johnson

Foreword by Dr. Ángel Manuel Rodríguez

Copyright © 2007 by Irma L. Johnson
Printed in the United States of America
All rights reserved.

Book Layout and Design:

A. Grace Brown, The Write Design, LLC
gbrown@writedesignllc.com

Photography Credits:

Cover photo: www.stockxpert.com. **Inside pages:** David Fournier, photofurnace.com – pages 18, 20, 40, 58; www.stockxpert.com – pages 24, 28, 31, 38, 44; www.morguefile.com – pages 22, 27, 36, 42, 48, 50, 52, 54, 57, 62, 70, 72, 74; www.photos.com – pages 12, 14, 16, 32, 34, 46, 64, 66, 68, 78; Irma Johnson – page 76.

For Information:

I Believe Poems
Poetic Words, LLC
P.O. Box 115 • Laurel, MD 20725
ibelievepoems@gmail.com

Seventh-day Adventist beliefs quoted from the *Seventh-day Adventist Church Manual, Revised 2005, 17th Edition*, Copyright © 2005 by the Secretariat, General Conference of Seventh-day Adventists. Unless otherwise indicated all Bible text references are from the King James Version of the Bible.

All scripture quotations, unless otherwise indicated, are taken from the HOLY BIBLE, NEW INTERNATIONAL VERSION®. NIV®. Copyright © 1973, 1978, 1984 by International Bible Society. Used by permission of Zondervan. All rights reserved.

ISBN 13: 978-0-9796754-0-9
ISBN 10: 0-9796754-0-5

This book is dedicated to
Kai, Kalen, and Kaden Johnson—our beautiful grandchildren,
and in memory of our daughter, Lena.

Acknowledgements

Special thanks to our Lord and Saviour, Jesus Christ for His love and guidance in every stage and event of our lives, and especially for His direction in the production of this book.

Heartfelt thanks to Dr. Ángel Rodríguez of the General Conference Biblical Research Institute and Dr. Lael Caesar of Andrews University, whose counsel and suggestions have been invaluable. Many thanks also to my husband, Alan B. Johnson, and our children Leanne and David Cort, Leon and Monica Johnson, and Lena Johnson for their support and work in this project.

I appreciate Grace Brown's (The Write Design, LLC) expertise in the design and completion of this project, and David Fournier's photography (Photo Furnace). This has been joyful experience, and hopefully will prove to be a blessing to all who read these pages.

Irma L. Johnson

Table of Contents

Foreword

Children are the most precious treasure the Lord has entrusted to the church and to their parents. Irma Johnson has produced a book that will certainly be a blessing to persons who work with children in our churches, and particularly to Christian parents as they pass on to their children the most basic elements of the biblical message of salvation through Christ. The book is a collection of poems, authored by her and attractively illustrated, telling the story of God's wonderful love in a simple and beautiful way. The readers have in their hands an excellent summary of the deep themes and doctrines of the Bible in the form of poems that will facilitate their memorization. This is another tool to aid parents in spiritual parenting, and that will reinforce in their own minds their understanding of the gospel of salvation.

Alongside the poems the readers will find scriptural references that will aid parents to find biblical texts that will further explain the concepts summarized in the poems. Through this volume we hope to awaken in both children and parents a genuine love for the Word of God and also strengthen their personal relationship with our dear Saviour. We anticipate that the book will be of assistance in communicating the message of the Bible to children in a simple and enjoyable way.

Ángel Manuel Rodríguez, Th.D, Director
Biblical Research Institute of the
General Conference of Seventh-day Adventists

I Believe...

POEMS OF FAITH FOR CHILDREN

Irma L. Johnson

Foreword by Dr. Ángel Manuel Rodríguez

The Holy Scriptures

The Holy Scriptures, Old and New Testaments, are the written Word of God given by divine inspiration through holy men of God who spoke and wrote as they were moved by the Holy Spirit. In this Word, God has committed to man the knowledge necessary for salvation. The Holy Scriptures are the infallible revelation of His will. They are the standard of character, the test of experience, the authoritative revealer of doctrines, and the trustworthy record of God's acts in history.

(2 Peter 1:20, 21; 2 Tim. 3:16, 17; Ps. 119:105; Prov. 30:5,6 ; Isa. 8:20; John 17:17; 1 Thess. 2:13; Heb. 4:12).

1
The Bible

Testament, Testament, Old and New
Make up the Bible, that is true.
Jesus told the prophets to write His Word,
So all children may learn of the Lord.

Testament, Testament, Old and New,
Teach me the story of love so true.
Jesus, Redeemer came to save,
And died on a cross, His life He gave.

Testament, Testament, Old and New,
Tell me how to live, and what to do.
Jesus, my example, a child like me,
Was obedient to the Testament, as I should be.

Your word is a lamp to my feet and a light for my path.

Psalm 119:105

The Trinity

There is one God: Father, Son, and Holy Spirit, a unity of three co-eternal Persons. God is immortal, all-powerful, all knowing, above all, and ever present. He is infinite and beyond human comprehension, yet known through His self-revelation. He is forever worthy of worship, adoration, and service by the whole creation.

(Deut. 6:4; Matt. 28:19; 2 Cor. 13:14; Eph. 4:4-6; 1 Peter 1:2; 1 Tim. 1:17; Rev. 14:7).

2
I Believe in Jesus

I believe in Jesus,
The Holy Spirit too,
And in God the Father,
Whose love is strong and true.
Jesus is my Saviour,
Holy Spirit is my guide,
Loving Father up in heaven
Sends angels to my side.
I will worship Jesus,
And live for Him each day.
Holy Spirit, and the Father
Give me grace and show the way.

Hear, O Israel: The LORD our God, the LORD is one.
Deuteronomy 6:4

The Father

God the eternal Father is the creator, source, sustainer, and sovereign of all creation. He is just and holy, merciful and gracious, slow to anger, and abounding in steadfast love and faithfulness. The qualities and powers exhibited in the Son and the Holy Spirit are also revelations of the Father.

(Gen. 1:1; Rev. 4:11; 1 Cor. 15:28; John 3:16; 1 John 4:8; 1 Tim. 1:17; Ex. 34:6, 7; John 14:9).

3
Our Father

Jesus taught us how to pray
To our Father up in heaven,
For He is holy, His kingdom comes,
And His name is reverend.

Each day He sends just what we need,
And in mercy forgives our wrong;
Helps us forgive like He forgave,
As His love in us grows strong.

Our Father is all powerful,
He's here, there, and everywhere.
He knows all about everything,
And we're in His tender care.

For God so loved the world that he gave his one and only Son, that whoever believes in him shall not perish but have eternal life.

John 3:16

The Son

God the eternal Son became incarnate in Jesus Christ. Through Him all things were created, the character of God is revealed, the salvation of humanity is accomplished, and the world is judged. Forever truly God, He became also truly man, Jesus the Christ. He was conceived of the Holy Spirit and born of the virgin, Mary. He lived and experienced temptation as a human being, but perfectly exemplified the righteousness and love of God. By His miracles He manifested God's power and was attested as God's promised Messiah. He suffered and died voluntarily on the cross for our sins and in our place, was raised from the dead, and ascended to minister in the heavenly sanctuary in our behalf. He will come again in glory for the final deliverance of His people and the restoration of all things.

(John 1:1-3, 14; Col. 1:15-19; John 10:30; 14:9; Rom. 6:23; 2 Cor. 5:17-19; John 5:22; Luke 1:35; Phil. 2:5-11; Heb. 2:9-18; 1 Cor. 15:3, 4; Heb. 8:1, 2; John 14:1-3).

4
The Son

Jesus is God from forever,
And He became a baby boy.
He grew up in wisdom and stature.
As our Saviour, He brings us joy.

He lived as a man and was tempted,
But never did any wrong.
He was meek and kind and obedient,
And loving Him, I can be strong.

Jesus is God from forever,
He bore my sins on the cross.
He arose from the dead a conqueror,
So that no one should be lost.

19

I and the

Father are one.

John 10:30

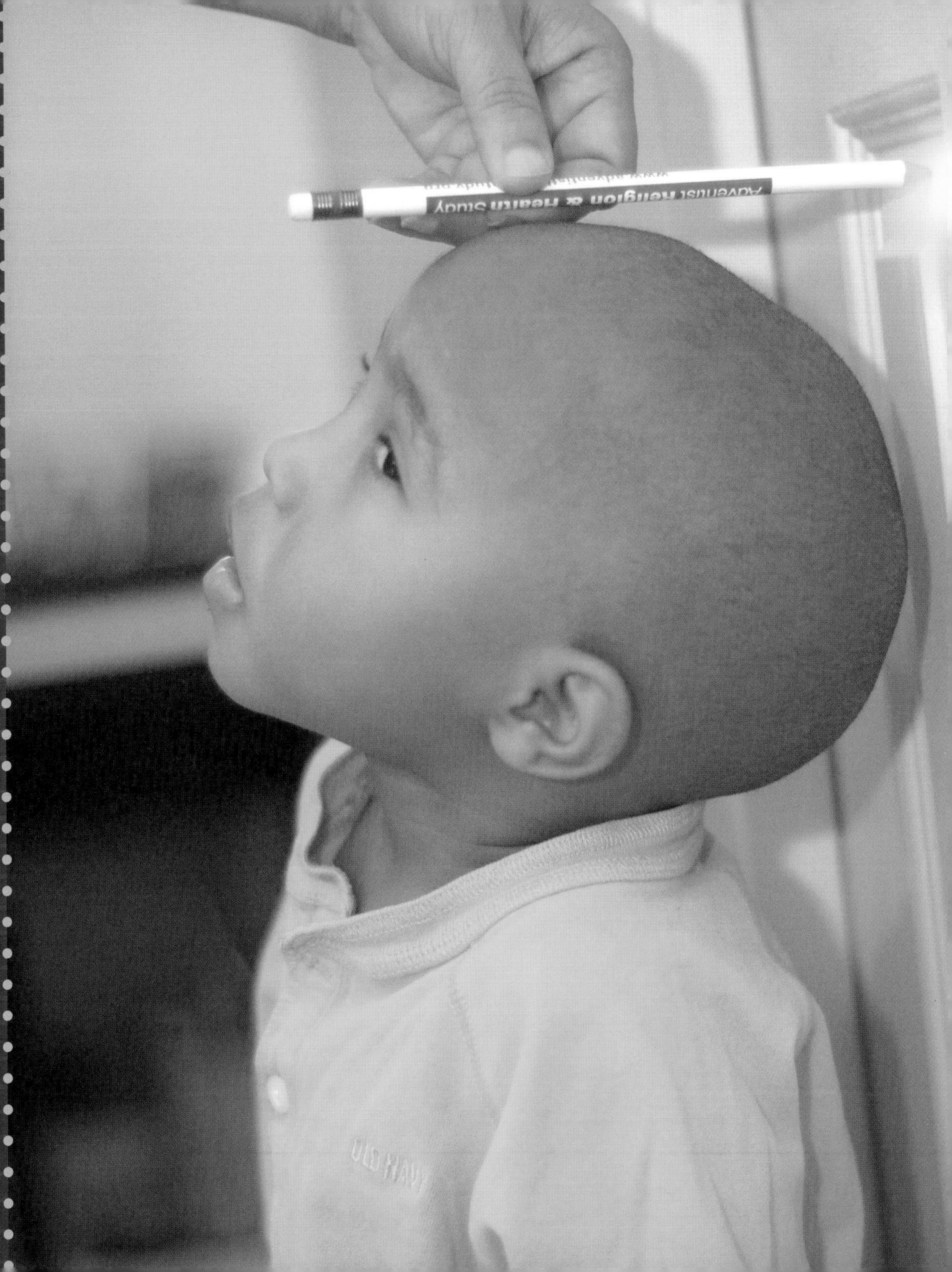
Adventist Religion & Health Study

When Jesus Was a Little Boy

When Jesus was a little boy,
He just loved to obey.
When His mother called Him,
He came right away.
I will be like Jesus,
For Jesus is my friend.
Jesus helps me to obey.
I will love Him to the end.

The Holy Spirit

God the eternal Spirit was active with the Father and the Son in Creation, incarnation, and redemption. He inspired the writers of Scripture. He filled Christ's life with power. He draws and convicts human beings, and those who respond He renews and transforms into the image of God. Sent by the Father and the Son to be always with His children, He extends spiritual gifts to the church, empowers it to bear witness to Christ, and in harmony with the Scriptures leads it into all truth.

(Gen. 1:1, 2; Luke 1:35; 4:18; Acts 10:38; 2 Peter 1:21; 2 Cor. 3:18; Eph. 4:11, 12; Acts 1:8; John 14:16-18, 26; 15:26, 27; 16:7-13).

5
My Comforter

The quiet voice that speaks truth to me
Is God's Holy Spirit, my guide,
Whom Jesus sent to comfort me.
He is always by my side.

He leads me when I do what's right,
And tells me when I am wrong,
And brings my praise to the Father,
When I pray or sing a song.

"But the Counselor, the Holy Spirit, whom the Father will send in my name, will teach you all things and remind you of everything I have said to you."

John 14:26

Creation

God is Creator of all things, and has revealed in Scripture the authentic account of His creative activity. In six days the Lord made "the heaven and the earth" and all living things upon the earth, and rested on the seventh day of that first week. Thus he established the Sabbath as a perpetual memorial of His completed creative work. The first man and woman were made in the image of God as the crowning work of Creation, given dominion over the world, and charged with responsibility to care for it. When the world was finished it was "very good," declaring the glory of God.

(Gen. 1, 2; Ex. 20:8-11; Ps. 19:1-6; 33:6, 9; Ps. 104; Heb. 11:3).

24

6
In the Beginning

In the beginning God spoke
And deep darkness went away
When He said, "Let there be light,"
On the very first earth-day.
And He divided the day and night,
And it was very good.

God spoke and from the midst of the waters
He formed the blue sky above
And spread the seas, rivers, and lakes
All over the brand new earth
This was the second day,
And it was very good.

God spoke again and dressed up the earth
In lots of pretty colors,
Flowers, vines, and soft green grass
Fruit trees, and plants and herbs.
This was the third day,
And it was very good.

In the beginning God created the heavens and the earth.

Genesis 1:1

25

Next God called the sun and moon,
Planets and shining stars
To rule the day and rule the night,
Lighting our world from afar.
This was the fourth day,
And it was very good.

God then spoke and in the waters
Were creatures of every kind,
He called forth birds to fly around,
And sing sweetly in trees and vines.
This was the fifth day,
And it was very good.

Next, God said, "Let the earth bring forth
Animals big and small."
And God made Adam and Eve
In His likeness, the best of all.
This was the sixth day,
And it was very good.

God rested on the seventh day
And gave Adam and Eve this time
To meet with Him in worship
And fellowship sublime.
This is the Sabbath day,
And it is very good.

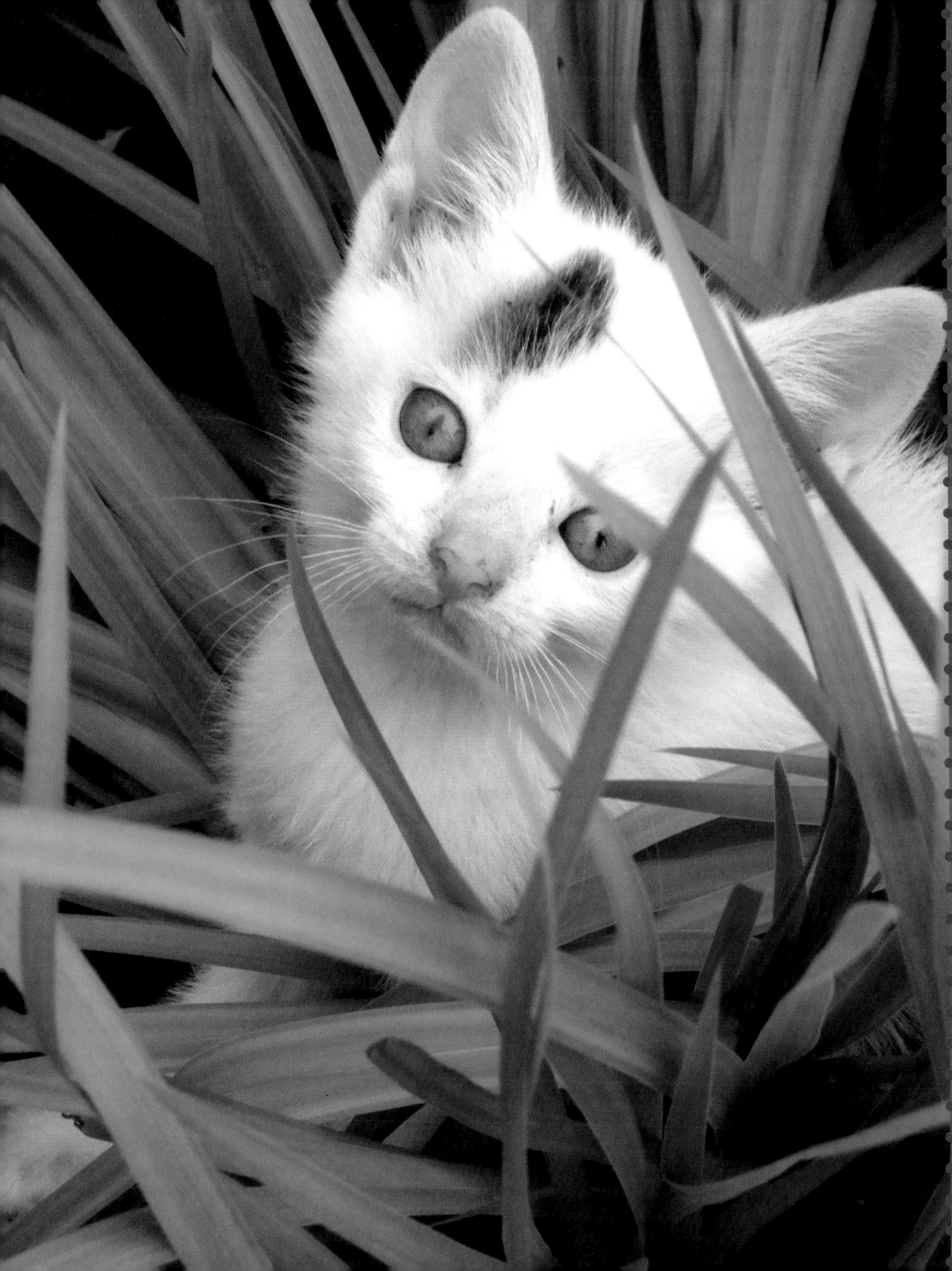

God's Creative Locker

I think… maybe,
God has a locker in which He keeps
His creative material,
And He has heaps and heaps:
Shimmering organza for gossamer wings,
Musical notes for every creature that sings;
Various sizes, textures, colors for petals,
Gold and silver, bronze – all kinds of metals;
Diamonds, emeralds, rubies – lots of stones;
Calcium and chemicals for making of bones;
Leaves of all sorts, all shades of green
For grasses, and trees and ferns can be seen.
God's locker is vast, seems there's no end;
There is light for suns, stars, and the angels He sends.
And there are hydrogen, and oxygen, so many gases
To make water and air; all there in great masses;
Hair, fur, feathers, and fish scales;
He has all in stock, in great big bales;
Tiny entities, like atoms and genes,
Vitamins, and amino acids for proteins.

The heavens declare the glory of God; the skies proclaim the work of his hands.
Psalm 19:1

29

Then there are forces He keeps, terrible, and dire,
Like hailstones, brimstone, wind, snow, rain, and fire!
He keeps the sounds of thunder, and the voice of the deep,
The sounds of many waters, and soft sighs of babies asleep.
In stock are moonlight, gentle wind, and dew,
And swans' down, mosses and lichens too.
The locker is lit with lightning's magnificent flashes,
Starlight, and clouds tied with silver sunshine sashes.
Yes, God has a locker in which He keeps
His creative material, He has heaps and heaps!

The Nature of Man

Man and woman were made in the image of God with individuality, the power and freedom to think and to do. Though created free beings, each is an indivisible unity of body, mind, and spirit, dependent upon God for life and breath and all else. When our first parents disobeyed God, they denied their dependence upon Him and fell from their high position under God. The image of God in them was marred and they became subject to death. Their descendants share this fallen nature and its consequences. They are born with weaknesses and tendencies to evil. But God in Christ reconciled the world to Himself and by His Spirit restores in penitent mortals the image of their Maker. Created for the glory of God, they are called to love Him and one another, and to care for their environment.

(Gen. 1:26-28; Gen. 2:7,15; Gen. 3; Ps. 8:4-8; Acts 17:24-28; Ps. 51:5,10; Rom. 5:12-17; 2 Cor. 5:19, 20; 1 John 4:7, 8, 11, 20).

7
Image of God

I am made in the image of God.
I can think and smile and walk.
I can see the lovely sunshine bright,
I can sing and shout and talk.

I am made in the image of God
To be strong and loving and kind.
I can make many things with my hands,
And store God's Word in my mind.

I am made in the image of God,
To be and look like Him,
To share His love with everyone,
And be pure and clean within.

Create in me a

pure heart, O

God, and renew

a steadfast

spirit within me.

Psalm 51:10

33

The Great Controversy

All humanity is now involved in a great controversy between Christ and Satan regarding the character of God, His law, and His sovereignty over the universe. This conflict originated in heaven when a created being, endowed with freedom of choice, in self-exaltation became Satan, God's adversary, and led into rebellion a portion of the angels. He introduced the spirit of rebellion into this world when he led Adam and Eve into sin. This human sin resulted in the distortion of the image of God in humanity, the disordering of the created world, and its eventual devastation at the time of the worldwide flood. Observed by the whole creation, this world became the arena of the universal conflict, out of which the God of love will ultimately be vindicated. To assist His people in this controversy, Christ sends the Holy Spirit and the loyal angels to guide, protect, and sustain them in the way of salvation.

(Rev. 12:4-9; Isa. 14:12-14; Eze. 28:12-18; Gen. 3; Rom. 1:19-32; 5:12-21; 8:19-22; Gen. 6-8; 2 Peter 3:6; 1 Cor. 4:9; Heb. 1:14).

34

8
Lucifer

Lucifer was an angel, who was very strong and bright.
He lived in heaven with Jesus, and his clothes were made of light.
At first he loved the Father, Holy Spirit, and the Son,
But he became unhappy, and was telling everyone
That the Father was not loving, was unkind and very unfair.
He made some angels wonder if God really loved and cared.
Soon there was war in heaven; Lucifer became the evil foe.
He was now the Devil and could stay in heaven no more.
Thrown out of highest heaven, to the earth he came
With his evil angels, and Satan is his name.
He taunts and tempts the children to be naughty and disobey,
But Jesus gives the power to live the right and holy way.
Now, good angels know the story, that God's love is true.
They don't believe the Devil, neither should I nor you.
Jesus won the battle in heaven and on earth.
He died on the cross to save us, and give us the new birth.
Born again Christians, living for our Lord,
We will go with Him to heaven, for we believe His Word.

For since the creation of the world God's invisible qualities — his eternal power and divine nature — have been clearly seen, being understood from what has been made, so that men are without excuse.

Romans 1:20

35

The Life, Death, and Resurrection of Christ

In Christ's life of perfect obedience to God's will, His suffering, death, and resurrection, God provided the only means of atonement for human sin, so that those who by faith accept this atonement may have eternal life, and the whole creation may better understand the infinite and holy love of the Creator. This perfect atonement vindicates the righteousness of God's law and the graciousness of His character; for it both condemns our sin and provides for our forgiveness. The death of Christ is substitutionary and expiatory, reconciling and transforming. The resurrection of Christ proclaims God's triumph over the forces of evil, and for those who accept the atonement assures their final victory over sin and death. It declares the Lordship of Jesus Christ, before whom every knee in heaven and on earth will bow.

(John 3:16; Isa. 53; 1 Peter 2:21, 22; 1 Cor. 15:3, 4, 20-22; 2 Cor. 5:14, 15, 19-21; Rom. 1:4; 3:25; 4:25; 8:3, 4; 1 John 2:2; 4:10; Col. 2:15; Phil. 2:6-11).

9
I Love Jesus Because...

I love Jesus because…
His life was lived for me,
His death paid for my sins
For all eternity.

I love Jesus because…
I am covered by His robe
Of righteousness and obedience,
He gave me the blessed hope.

I love Jesus because…
When He arose from the grave,
He conquered Satan and death;
His grace and love prevailed.

I love Jesus because…
I am always safe in His care.
He is my friend and Saviour,
He goes with me everywhere.

For God so loved the world that he gave his one and only Son that whoever believes in him shall not perish but have eternal life.

John 3:16

The Experience of Salvation

In infinite love and mercy God made Christ, who knew no sin, to be sin for us, so that in Him we might be made the righteousness of God. Led by the Holy Spirit we sense our need, acknowledge our sinfulness, repent of our transgressions, and exercise faith in Jesus as Lord and Christ, as Substitute and Example. This faith which receives salvation comes through the divine power of the Word and is the gift of God's grace. Through Christ we are justified, adopted as God's sons and daughters, and delivered from the lordship of sin. Through the Spirit we are born again and sanctified; the Spirit renews our minds, writes God's law of love in our hearts, and we are given the power to live a holy life. Abiding in Him we become partakers of the divine nature and have the assurance of salvation now and in the judgment.

(2 Cor. 5:17-21; John 3:16; Gal. 1:4; 4:4-7;
Titus 3:3-7; John 16:8; Gal. 3:13, 14;
1 Peter 2:21, 22; Rom. 10:17; Luke 17:5;
Mark 9:23, 24; Eph. 2:5-10; Rom. 3:21-26;
Col. 1:13, 14; Rom. 8:14-17; Gal. 3:26; John 3:3-8;
1 Peter 1:23; Rom. 12:2; Heb. 8:7-12;
Eze 36:25-27; 2 Peter 1:3, 4; Rom. 8:1-4; 5:6-10).

10
Salvation

Jesus left bright heaven,
And came to this dark world of ours,
He left angels and glory,
And laid aside His powers.

He, who was pure and sinless,
Became sin for us,
To suffer and die in our place
On a horrible, cruel cross.

He did it so that in Him
We might be righteous before God,
As we accept His forgiveness,
And have faith in His spilled blood.

In Jesus we are adopted,
Children of the heavenly King!
Thankful for His atonement,
His praises we'll always sing.

Therefore, if any-

one is in Christ,

he is a new creation;

the old has gone,

the new has come!

2 Corinthians 5:17

39

Growing in Christ

By His death on the cross Jesus triumphed over the forces of evil. He who subjugated the demonic spirits during His earthly ministry has broken their power and made certain their ultimate doom. Jesus' victory gives us victory over the evil forces that still seek to control us, as we walk with Him in peace, joy, and assurance of His love. Now the Holy Spirit dwells within us and empowers us. Continually committed to Jesus as our Saviour and Lord, we are set free from the burden of our past deeds. No longer do we live in the darkness, fear of evil powers, ignorance, and meaninglessness of our former way of life. In this new freedom in Jesus, we are called to grow into the likeness of His character, communing with Him daily in prayer, feeding on His Word, meditating on it, and on His providence, singing His praises, gathering together for worship, and participating in the mission of the church. As we give ourselves in loving service to those around us and in witnessing to His salvation, His constant presence with us through the Spirit transforms every moment and every task into a spiritual experience.

(Ps. 1:1, 2; Ps. 23:4; Ps. 77:11, 12; Col. 1:13, 14; Col. 2:6, 14, 15; Luke 10:17-20; Eph. 5:19, 20; Eph. 6:12-18; 1 Thess. 5:23; 2 Peter 2:9; 3:18; 2 Cor. 3:17, 18; Phil. 3:7-14; 1 Thess. 5:16-18; Matt. 20:25-28; John 20:21; Gal. 5:22-25).

11
Growing in Christ

By His death on the cross, Jesus won the big fight.
His weapon was love and His armor was light.

He broke the demon power that makes people sin.
He frees all the prisoners so in Him they can win.

Jesus gained the victory, we do not have to fear.
Evil cannot control us, when we are in His care.

We walk in peace with Jesus, wrapped up in His love.
His Holy Spirit fills us with power from above.

We grow more like Jesus, when we sing and pray,
And read the Bible daily, and live the kind and loving way.

Blessed is the man who does not walk in the counsel of the wicked or stand in the way of sinners or sit in the seat of mockers. But his delight is in the law of the LORD, and on his law he meditates day and night.

Psalm 1: 1, 2

The Church

The church is the community of believers who confess Jesus Christ as Lord and Saviour. In continuity with the people of God in Old Testament times, we are called out from the world; and we join together for worship, for fellowship, for instruction in the Word, for the celebration of the Lord's Supper, for service to all mankind, and for the worldwide proclamation of the gospel. The church derives its authority from Christ, who is the incarnate Word, and from the Scriptures, which are the written Word. The church is God's family; adopted by Him as children, its members live on the basis of the new covenant. The church is the body of Christ, a community of faith of which Christ Himself is the Head. The church is the bride for whom Christ died that He might sanctify and cleanse her. At His return in triumph, He will present her to Himself a glorious church, the faithful of all the ages, the purchase of His blood, not having spot or wrinkle, but holy and without blemish.

(Gen. 12:3; Acts 7:38; Eph. 4:11-15; 3:8-11; Matt. 28:19, 20; 16:13-20; 18:18; Eph. 2:19-22; Eph. 1:22, 23; 5:23-27; Col. 1:17, 18).

12
God's Church

God's church is His family, who lives everywhere,
Sharing with all the gospel, showing His tender care.

Like the people in the Bible, called out from the world,
God's church joins in worship, and in fellowship and love.

In the study of His Word, God's family learns His ways,
And meets Him in Communion on His holy Sabbath days.

God's church is His body, He is the only Head.
His church is also His bride, whom He is coming back to wed.

I am a part of God's church, to minister in His name.
Lord, help me to be always faithful, until You come again.

In him the whole building is joined together and rises to become a holy temple in the LORD. And in him you too are being built together to become a dwelling in which God lives by his Spirit.

Ephesians 2: 21–22

The Remnant and Its Mission

The universal church is composed of all who truly believe in Christ, but in the last days, a time of widespread apostasy, a remnant has been called out to keep the commandments of God and the faith of Jesus. This remnant announces the arrival of the judgment hour, proclaims salvation through Christ, and heralds the approach of His second advent. This proclamation is symbolized by the three angels of Revelation 14; it coincides with the work of judgment in heaven and results in a work of repentance and reform on earth. Every believer is called to have a personal part in this worldwide witness.

(Rev. 12:17; 14:6-12; 18:1-4; 2 Cor. 5:10; Jude 3, 14; 1 Peter 1:16-19; 2 Peter 3:10-14; Rev. 21:1-14).

13
Go Into All the World

Go out into all the world,
And let the people know,
That Jesus came to seek and save
Sinners, high and low.

Teach them it's the last days,
Jesus is coming soon.
It is the time of judgment,
There'll be signs in sun and moon!

On the earth distress of nations,
Makes men die of fear.
Preach to all about God's law,
He wants them all to hear.

Teach about the faith of Jesus,
That will carry each one through.
Be a faithful witness,
In what Jesus wants you to do.

He said to them,

"Go into all the

world and preach

the good news to

all creation..."

Mark 16: 15

Unity in the Body of Christ

The church is one body with many members, called from every nation, kindred, tongue, and people. In Christ we are a new creation, distinctions of race, culture, learning, and nationality, and differences between high and low, rich and poor, male and female, must not be divisive among us. We are all equal in Christ, who by one Spirit has bonded us into one fellowship with Him and with one another; we are to serve and be served without partiality or reservation. Through the revelation of Jesus Christ in the Scriptures, we share the same faith and hope, and reach out in one witness to all. This unity has its source in the oneness of the triune God, who has adopted us as His children.

(Rom. 12:4, 5; 1 Cor. 12:12-14; Matt. 28:19, 20; Ps. 133:1; 2 Cor. 5:16, 17; Acts 17:26, 27; Gal. 3:27, 29; Col. 3:10-15; Eph. 4:14-16; 4:1-6; John 17:20-23).

14
Jesus Christ Unites Us

We are many members,
Called out from every nation,
From kindred, tongues, and people,
Children of God's creation;

So different in tastes and talents,
In culture, gender, and race;
Bonded by God's Holy Spirit,
Blessed by His saving grace.

We are to serve, and be served as equals,
The same faith and hope sharing,
Reaching out in one witness,
For each other truly caring.

Jesus is the One who unites us.
In Him we all live and move.
Together, we are going to heaven,
Together, we will live in love.

How good and pleasant it is when brothers live together in unity!

Psalm 133:1

Baptism

By baptism we confess our faith in the death and resurrection of Jesus Christ, and testify of our death to sin and of our purpose to walk in newness of life. Thus we acknowledge Christ as Lord and Saviour, become His people, and are received as members by His church. Baptism is a symbol of our union with Christ, the forgiveness of our sins, and our reception of the Holy Spirit. It is by immersion in water and is contingent on an affirmation of faith in Jesus and evidence of repentance of sin. It follows instruction in the Holy Scriptures and acceptance of their teachings.

(Rom. 6:1-6; Col. 2:12, 13; Acts 16:30-33; 22:16; Acts 2:38; Matt. 28:19, 20).

15
Baptism

One day, Jesus went to Jordan, a river deep and wide,
And John the Baptist was there, Jesus went right up to his side.

"Behold, the Lamb of God," John exclaimed to everyone,
"He will take away all sin, the kingdom of God has come."

Jesus said, "Please baptize me in the river over there."
John did not feel worthy, he was filled with holy fear.

But they went into the river, and John baptized his Lord,
Jesus was our example in obeying God's holy Word.

The Holy Spirit rested on Him, the Father's voice was clear,
"This is my Beloved Son," for everyone to hear.

I will follow Jesus, and be baptized just like Him,
And the Father up in heaven, will bless me too like Him.

We were therefore buried with him through baptism into death in order that, just as Christ was raised from the dead through the glory of the Father, we too may live a new life.

Romans 6:4

49

The Lord's Supper

The Lord's Supper is a participation in the emblems of the body and blood of Jesus as an expression of faith in Him, our Lord and Saviour. In this experience of communion Christ is present to meet and strengthen His people. As we partake, we joyfully proclaim the Lord's death until He comes again. Preparation for the Supper includes self-examination, repentance and confession. The Master ordained the service of foot washing to signify renewed cleansing, to express a willingness to serve one another in Christlike humility, and to unite our hearts in love. The Communion service is open to all believing Christians.

(1 Cor. 10:16, 17; 11:23-30; Matt. 26:17-30; Rev. 3:20; John 6:48-63; 13:1-17).

50

16
I Want Jesus to Wash My Feet

I want Jesus to wash my feet,
Like He washed the disciples of old,
And when I drink the Communion wine,
I know He cleanses my soul.
I eat the Communion bread,
And remember for me He died.
I am looking forward one day
To eat and drink it by His side.

"You call me 'Teacher' and 'Lord,' and rightly so, for that is what I am. Now that I, your Lord and Teacher, have washed your feet, you also should wash one another's feet."

John 13:13-14

Spiritual Gifts and Ministries

God bestows upon all members of His church in every age spiritual gifts which each member is to employ in loving ministry for the common good of the church and of humanity. Given by the agency of the Holy Spirit, who apportions to each member as He wills, the gifts provide all abilities and ministries needed by the church to fulfill its divinely ordained functions. According to the Scriptures, these gifts include such ministries as faith, healing, prophecy, proclamation, teaching, administration, reconciliation, compassion, and self-sacrificing service and charity for the help and encouragement of people. Some members are called of God and endowed by the Spirit for functions recognized by the church in pastoral, evangelistic, apostolic, and teaching ministries particularly needed to equip the members for service, to build up the church to spiritual maturity, and to foster unity of the faith and knowledge of God. When members employ these spiritual gifts as faithful stewards of God's varied grace, the church is protected from the destructive influence of false doctrine, grows with a growth that is from God, and is built up in faith and love.

(Rom. 12:4-8; 1 Cor. 12:9-11, 27, 28; Eph. 4:8, 11-16; Acts 6:1-7; 1 Tim. 3:1-13; 1 Peter 4:10, 11).

52

17
The Gift of Helps

Jesus wants me to be loving;
Jesus wants me to be kind.
Jesus wants me to be helping,
Like He was all the time.

I help when I put my toys in the box,
I help put away my shoes and socks.
I help my Mom make up my bed.
I help my Dad plant a garden bed.

I help when I visit my neighbor,
Who is sick across the way,
And sing a song of joy for her,
To brighten up her day.

I am glad I have the gift of helps,
I use it all I can
To share, bless, and give God's love,
And tell of the Son of Man.

Now to each one the manifestation of the Spirit is given for the common good.

1 Corinthians 12:7

53

The Gift of Prophecy

One of the gifts of the Holy Spirit is prophecy. This gift is an identifying mark of the remnant church and was manifested in the ministry of Ellen G. White. As the Lord's messenger, her writings are a continuing and authoritative source of truth which provide for the church comfort, guidance, instruction, and correction. They also make clear that the Bible is the standard by which all teaching and experience must be tested.

(Joel 2:28, 29; Acts 2:14-21; Heb. 1:1-3; Rev. 12:17; Rev. 19:10).

54

18
Prophecy

Prophecy is a very big word,
What does it mean?
It means to tell the future,
What was said, must then be seen.

Prophecy is also more
Than just to tell the future;
It is God's way of guiding
And instructing all His people.

In the Bible, holy men
Wrote what they were told
By the Holy Spirit;
Their words are true and bold.

"*And afterward,*

I will pour out

my Spirit on all

people. Your

sons and

daughters

will prophesy,

your old men

will dream

dreams, your

young men will

see visions."

Joel 2:28

55

The testimony of Jesus
Is the Spirit of Prophecy;
And Jesus helps His children
His commandments to obey.

Prophecies are fulfilling,
Events have come to pass
Just as they were written,
From the first and to the last.

They are sure, and timely,
And still they let us know
What will happen in the future,
And the way we ought to go.

I desire to do your will, O my God; your law is within my heart.

Psalm 40:8

The Law of God

The great principles of God's law are embodied in the Ten Commandments and exemplified in the life of Christ. They express God's love, will, and purposes concerning human conduct and relationships and are binding upon all people in every age. These precepts are the basis of God's covenant with His people and the standard in God's judgment. Through the agency of the Holy Spirit they point out sin and awaken a sense of need for a Saviour. Salvation is all of grace and not of works, but its fruitage is obedience to the Commandments. This obedience develops Christian character and results in a sense of well-being. It is an evidence of our love for the Lord and our concern for our fellow men. The obedience of faith demonstrates the power of Christ to transform lives, and therefore strengthens Christian witness.

(Ex. 20:1-17; Ps. 40, 7, 8; Matt. 22:36-40; Deut. 28:1-14; Matt. 5:17-20; Heb. 8: 8-10; John 15:7-10; Eph. 2:8-10; 1 John 5:3; Rom. 8:3, 4; Ps. 19:7-14).

19
Because We Love Him

The law of God is a law of love,
Which He wants us to obey.
Because we love Him,
We will not have other gods any day.

We will not make idols,
Nor bow down to wood or stone,
For the Lord our God is a jealous God,
Who wants us to serve Him alone.

Because we love Him,
We will not take His holy name in vain.
Our lips will always speak His praise,
As a witness again, and again.

We'll remember the holy Sabbath,
And that He made the whole wide earth,
And spend the seventh day worshiping,
Resting from six days of work.

The law of the Lord is perfect, reviving the soul. The statutes of the LORD are trustworthy, making wise the simple.

Psalm 19:7

59

Because we love Him,
We will honor our father and mother too,
And do our best to make them proud
Of all we try to do.

Because we love Him
We will not take another person's life,
Nor even speak words to wound and hurt,
That cut the heart like a knife.

And when we are married,
We will stay always faithful and true
To the one we have vowed to love,
And our vows always renew.

The Lord does not want us to steal, or cheat,
And be guilty of doing wrong.
When we are honest, He is glorified,
And He makes us very strong.

Because we love Him,
We won't tell lies against our friends and others.
He wants us ever to speak the truth,
Be examples to our sisters and brothers.

And when we see our neighbors
With things that are pretty, expensive, and fine,
We will not be covetous or envious,
Because we love our Saviour Divine.

Jesus said, if you love Me,
My commandments you will keep.
My strength is all-sufficient,
My grace is your victory.

The Sabbath

The beneficent Creator, after the six days of Creation, rested on the seventh day and instituted the Sabbath for all people as a memorial of Creation. The fourth commandment of God's unchangeable law requires the observance of this seventh-day Sabbath as the day of rest, worship, and ministry in harmony with the teaching and practice of Jesus, the Lord of the Sabbath. The Sabbath is a day of delightful communion with God and one another. It is a symbol of our redemption in Christ, a sign of our sanctification, a token of our allegiance, and a foretaste of our eternal future in God's kingdom. The Sabbath is God's perpetual sign of His eternal covenant between Him and His people, Joyful observance of this holy time from evening to evening, sunset to sunset is a celebration of God's creative and redemptive acts.

(Gen. 2:1-3; Ex. 20:8-11; Luke 4:16; Isa. 56:5, 6; Isa. 58:13, 14; Matt. 12:1-12; Ex. 31:13-17; Eze. 20:12, 20; Deut. 5:12-15; Heb. 4:1-11; Lev. 23:32; Mark 1:32).

20
Sabbath

Sabbath is my favorite day!
I think of God and heaven.
I look around, I take a walk,
And admire His creation.

Sabbath comes with the set of sun
Every Friday afternoon.
This day is so very special,
It cannot come too soon!

Like Jesus did, I go to church,
I sing, and praise, and pray.
I am so happy that Jesus thought
To share with me His day.

And during the week, I do prepare
For the coming of Day-Seven.
I do all my work, put away my toys,
And look forward to a bit of heaven.

Jesus is my Sabbath rest,
He gives me joy, and peace.
I love my Saviour, I love His day,
Oh, that it will never cease!

"Also I gave them my Sabbaths as a sign between us, so they would know that I the LORD made them holy."

Ezekiel 20:12

63

Stewardship

We are God's stewards, entrusted by Him with time and opportunities, abilities and possessions, and the blessings of the earth and its resources. We are responsible to Him for their proper use. We acknowledge God's ownership by faithful service to Him and our fellow men, and by returning tithes and giving offerings for the proclamation of His gospel and the support and growth of His church. Stewardship is a privilege given to us by God for nurture in love and the victory over selfishness and covetousness. The steward rejoices in the blessings that come to others as a result of his faithfulness.

(Gen. 1:26-28; 2:15; 1 Chron. 29:14; Hag. 1:3-11; Mal. 3:8-12; 1 Cor. 9:9-14; Matt. 23:23; 2 Cor. 8:1-15; Rom. 15:26, 27).

64

21
I Am a Manager

Jesus made me to be His manager,
To help care for the whole wide earth,
To keep things clean, and in order,
And enjoy it for all that it's worth.

I must manage my time, my actions,
My treasures, and body temple too,
For I am a steward of Jesus
In everything I do.

So, I learn not to be selfish,
But to be thoughtful of others' needs.
I share, and bring them happiness,
And find joy in doing good deeds.

God blessed them and said to them, "Be fruitful and increase in number; fill the earth and subdue it. Rule over the fish of the sea and the birds of the air and over every living creature that moves on the ground."

Genesis 1:28

65

Christian Behavior

We are called to be a godly people who think, feel, and act in harmony with the principles of heaven. For the Spirit to recreate in us the character of our Lord we involve ourselves only in those things which will produce Christlike purity, health, and joy in our lives. This means that our amusement and entertainment should meet the highest standards of Christian taste and beauty. While recognizing cultural differences, our dress is to be simple, modest, and neat, befitting those whose true beauty does not consist of outward adornment but in the imperishable ornament of a gentle and quiet spirit. It also means that because our bodies are the temples of the Holy Spirit we are to care for them intelligently. Along with adequate exercise and rest, we are to adopt the most healthful diet possible and abstain from the unclean foods identified in the Scriptures. Since alcoholic beverages, tobacco, and the irresponsible

22
My Body Is a Temple

My body is God's temple, I must eat that which is good,
I'm glad Jesus gave us nuts, vegetables, and fruit.
I should not eat between meals to give my tummy a rest
I must drink lots of water, and exercise my best.

I am going to be so careful of what I watch, and read,
So Satan may not plant in my mind an evil seed.
The clothes I choose to wear will be simple, neat, and clean
Jesus' beauty must shine through, His way in me be seen.

Alcohol, smoking, and doing drugs–
I will stay away from such things,
For they are Satan's weapons
And great unhappiness bring.

Jesus wants me to be happy in all I say and do,
He wants me to be healthy, and He will bless me too.
He wants me to be pure in heart, like He was as a child
Jesus, please help me to live for You all the while.

Do you not know that your body is a temple of the Holy Spirit, who is in you, whom you have received from God?

1 Corinthians 6:19

67

use of drugs and narcotics are harmful to our bodies, we are to abstain from them as well. Instead, we are to engage in whatever brings our thoughts and bodies into the discipline of Christ, who desires our wholesomeness, joy, and goodness.

(Rom. 12:1, 2; 1 John 2:6;
Eph. 5:1-21; Phil. 4:8; 2 Cor. 10:5;
2 Cor. 6:14-7:1; 1 Peter 3:1-4;
1 Cor. 6:19, 20; 10:31; Lev. 11:1-47;
3 John 2).

Marriage and the Family

Marriage was divinely established in Eden and affirmed by Jesus to be a lifelong union between a man and a woman in loving companionship. For the Christian a marriage commitment is to God as well as to the spouse, and should be entered into only between partners who share a common faith. Mutual love, honor, respect, and responsibility are the fabric of this relationship, which is to reflect the love, sanctity, closeness, and permanence of the relationship between Christ and His church. Regarding divorce, Jesus taught that the person who divorces a spouse, except for fornication, and marries another, commits adultery. Although some family relationships may fall short of the ideal, marriage partners who fully commit themselves to each other in Christ may achieve loving unity through the guidance of the Spirit and the nurture of the church. God blesses the family and intends that its members shall assist each other toward complete maturity. Parents are to bring up their children to love and

23
The First Wedding

God made Adam, the very first man
When He formed and fashioned red dirt,
And breathed in his nostrils the breath of life,
And awoke him to live on the earth.

Adam admired the animals fair
That roamed in the Garden of Eden
But he could not find one among them
To be his own life companion.

So God put him to sleep the very same day,
And took a rib right out of his side,
And made a wonderful woman to love.
She became his beautiful bride.

Eve was flesh of his flesh, and bone of his bones,
His helpmeet, intelligent, and caring.
They walked hand in hand the rest of their lives,
Loving, and learning, and sharing.

This is the pattern God set for us all
From since the very beginning.
We will be blessed, as we follow His plan,
And have families that are happy and loving.

For this reason a man will leave his father and mother and be united with his wife, and they will become one flesh.
Genesis 2:24

obey the Lord. By their example and their words they are to teach them that Christ is a loving disciplinarian, ever tender and caring, who wants them to become members of His body, the family of God. Increasing family closeness is one of the earmarks of the final gospel message.

(Gen. 2:18-25; Matt. 19:3-9; John 2:1-11; 2 Cor. 6:14; Eph. 5:21-33; Matt 5:31, 32; Mark 10:11,12; Luke 16:18; 1 Cor. 7:10, 11; Ex. 20:12; Eph. 6:1-4; Deut. 6:5-9; Prov. 22:6; Mal. 4:5, 6).

Christ's Ministry in the Heavenly Sanctuary

There is a sanctuary in heaven, the true tabernacle which the Lord set up and not man. In it Christ ministers on our behalf, making available to believers the benefits of His atoning sacrifice offered once for all on the cross. He was inaugurated as our great High Priest and began His intercessory ministry at the time of His ascension. In 1844, at the end of the prophetic period of 2300 days, He entered the second and last phase of His atoning ministry. It is a work of investigative judgment which is part of the ultimate disposition of all sin, typified by the cleansing of the ancient Hebrew sanctuary on the Day of Atonement. In that typical service the sanctuary was cleansed with the blood of animal sacrifices, but the heavenly things are purified with the perfect sacrifice of the blood of Jesus. The investigative judgment reveals to heavenly intelligences who among the dead are asleep in Christ and therefore, in Him, are deemed worthy to have a part in the first resurrection. It also makes manifest who, among the living are abiding in Christ, keeping the commandments of

24
The Sanctuary

In heaven there's a sanctuary, where Jesus intercedes.
He is the Lamb, and He is the Priest, and for me He pleads.

In heaven there's a sanctuary, and there's the Mercy Seat.
The angels gather around the throne, see the Sacrifice complete.

The Bread of Life is Jesus Christ, His incense blends my prayers.
The Lamp sheds the Light of Life, there's glory everywhere.

The sanctuary teaches me of grace full and free.
The righteousness of Christ is mine. It's all about saving me.

He said in a loud voice, "Fear God and give him glory, because the hour of his judgment has come..."

Revelation 14:7

71

God and the faith of Jesus, and in Him, therefore, are ready for translation into His everlasting kingdom. This judgment vindicates the justice of God in saving those who believe in Jesus. It declares that those who have remained loyal to God shall receive the kingdom. The completion of this ministry of Christ will mark the close of human probation before the Second Advent.

(Heb. 1:3; Heb. 2:16, 17; Heb. 4:14-16; Heb. 8:1-5; Heb. 9:11-28; Heb. 10:19-22; Dan. 7:9-27; 8:13, 14; 9:24-27; Eze. 4:6; Lev. 16; Rev. 14:6, 7; 20:12; 14:12; 22:12).

The Second Coming of Christ

The second coming of Christ is the blessed hope of the church, the grand climax of the gospel. The Saviour's coming will be literal, personal, visible and worldwide. When He returns, the righteous dead will be resurrected, and together with the righteous living will be glorified and taken to heaven, but the unrighteous will die. The almost complete fulfillment of most lines of prophecy, together with the present condition of the world, indicates that Christ's coming is imminent. The time of that event has not been revealed, and we are therefore exhorted to be ready at all times.

(Titus 2:13; Heb. 9:28; John 14:1-3; Acts 1:9-11; Matt. 24:14; Rev. 1:7; Matt. 24:43, 44; 1 Thess. 4:13-18; 1 Cor. 15:51-54; 2 Thess. 1:7-10; 2:8; Rev. 14:14-20; 19:11-21; Matt. 24; Mark 13; Luke 21; 2 Tim. 3:1-5; 1 Thess. 5:1-6).

25
Jesus Is Coming Back

When lightning flashes across the sky,
It reminds me that Jesus will come.
He promised He will come again
To take His children home.

Everyone will see the little black cloud
Appearing in the east.
There will be a trumpet blast
To resurrect the greatest and least.

While sinners are running to the rocks to hide,
Saved children look up and say,
"This is our God, we've waited for Him.
We love Him even more today."

Come then, Jesus, we are waiting for You,
Singing and praising Your name,
Telling others of Your love for them,
While we wait for Your coming again.

In my Father's house are many rooms; if it were not so, I would have told you. I am going there to prepare a place for you. And if I go and prepare a place for you, I will come back and take you to be with me that you also may be where I am.

John 14:2, 3

73

Death and Resurrection

The wages of sin is death. But God, who alone is immortal, will grant eternal life to His redeemed. Until that day death is an unconscious state for all people. When Christ, who is our life, appears, the resurrected righteous and the living righteous will be glorified and caught up to meet their Lord. The second resurrection, the resurrection of the unrighteous, will take place a thousand years later.

(Rom. 6:23; 1 Tim. 6:15, 16; Eccl. 9:5, 6; Ps. 146:3, 4; John 11:11-14; Col. 3:4; 1 Cor. 15:51-54; 1 Thess. 4:13-17; John 5:28, 29; Rev. 20:1-10).

26
My Friend Died

My friend died,
And everybody cried.
She is asleep in Jesus,
Waiting in the ground
For Jesus second coming,
And the angel trumpet sound.
Jesus will awaken her;
And all who love the Lord
Will live with God forever,
As it is written in His Word.

Brothers, we do not want you to be ignorant about those who fall asleep, or to grieve like the rest of men, who have no hope.

1 Thessalonians 4:13

The Millennium and the End of Sin

The millennium is the thousand-year reign of Christ with His saints in heaven between the first and second resurrections. During this time the wicked dead will be judged; the earth will be utterly desolate, without living human inhabitants, but occupied by Satan and his angels. At its close Christ with His saints and the Holy City will descend from heaven to earth. The unrighteous dead will then be resurrected, and with Satan and his angels will surround the city; but fire from God will consume them and cleanse the earth. The universe will thus be freed of sin and sinners forever.

(Rev. 20; 1 Cor 6:2, 3; Jer. 4:23-26; Rev. 21:1-5; Mal. 4:1; Eze. 28:18, 19).

76

27
A Thousand Years in Heaven

The Bible teaches me that soon Jesus will come again,
And I will go to heaven with Him, one thousand years to reign.

The earth will be left empty and bare, with Satan and imps alone,
No one to tempt, no one to scare, 'til one thousand years are gone.

Then we will come down in the city of God with the angels, and Jesus too.
The wicked dead will arise again, their bad thoughts and acts to do.

But Jesus will send cleansing fire to burn away all sin,
And those who followed Satan's plan will sadly be with him.

"Just and true are Thy ways, O God," they will all confess.
They know they chose the second death, when they chose unrighteousness.

Jesus came to earth to save, and poured His love from the cross.
He calls, and pleads and gives His grace, so that no one should be lost.

I will give my heart to Him, and live for Him each day,
Looking forward to the millennium, as I walk the narrow way.

Blessed and holy are those who have part in the first resurrection. The second death has no power over them, but they will be priests of God and of Christ and will reign with him for a thousand years.

Revelation 20:6

77

The New Earth

On the new earth, in which righteousness dwells, God will provide an eternal home for the redeemed and a perfect environment for everlasting life, love, joy, and learning in His presence. For here God Himself will dwell with His people, and suffering and death will have passed away. The great controversy will be ended, and sin will be no more. All things, animate and inanimate, will declare that God is love, and He shall reign forever. Amen.

(2 Peter 3:13; Isa. 35; 65:17-25; Matt. 5:5; Rev. 21:1-7; 22:1-5; 11:15).

28
A Brand New Earth!

God will make a brand new earth, when the world is cleansed by fire.
Only righteousness will reign, and nothing else will die.

New birds will flitter everywhere, new butterflies and bees,
New flowers, grass, animals, fish, water, vines, and trees.

And I will play with tame tigers, I will walk on gemstones bright.
Gold and diamonds will be everywhere, reflecting heaven's light.

The new earth, my new home, is Jesus' gift to me,
And to my Mom, and to my Dad, and all my family.

We'll build our house, and plant and reap fruits, and nuts, and grain,
And we'll learn lots and lots about God's love supreme.

And on Sabbath, from week to week, up the highway grand,
We'll go to worship Jesus in the New Jerusalem.

We'll pray, and sing, and play our harps, with angels joining in.
We will be with Jesus every day, because we all love Him.

Then I saw a new heaven and a new earth, for the first heaven and the first earth had passed away, and there was no longer any sea.

Revelation 21:1

79

About the Author

Irma L. Johnson loves children, and believes in spiritual parenting. She passionately counsels parents to focus on their responsibility of making use of the precious early years of childhood, when the "soil" of little lives is fertile ground for planting the seeds of the gospel.

The enjoyment of writing poems and rhymes has been a wonderful experience for Irma. She writes when deeply impressed. She believes the Lord gave her the "assignment" to write the poems and rhymes in this book and have the book sent all over the world for the benefit of both parents and their children.

She ministers alongside her husband, Pastor Alan B. Johnson, in the Mitchellville Church in Maryland. They are parents of three adult children, Leanne Johnson-Cort and husband, David; Leon Johnson and wife, Monica; and Dr. Lena Johnson (now asleep in Jesus). Their grandchildren are Kai, Kalen, and Kaden, children of Leon and Monica.

For the 17 years that I have known her, Irma has been to me mother, sister, friend, confidante, and a veritable fount of wisdom. Her unique principles of child rearing that she has shared with me have been so invaluable, so sound, I cannot imagine how I would have raised my children without her.

Irma has worked at Adventist Risk Management, Inc., at the General Conference of Seventh-day Adventists since 1986. She is a senior property/casualty claims examiner.

Dr. Lavern Bentt-Bruce
Stanford University MD (1987)
anesthesiologist, pain management specialist